Written by Elsie Egermeier
Illustrated by Wilson Williams, Jr.

Edited by Robin Fogle
Design Layout by Christian Elden

ISBN: 978-1-59317-705-8

PUBLISHED BY

Warner Press, Inc.
1201 E. 5th Street
Anderson, IN 46012

Printed in the United States of America
Tracking # 469740110447

The Angel Visits Mary

Matthew 1:18-25; Luke 1:26-56

A young woman named Mary was engaged to marry Joseph, a carpenter in the city of Nazareth in Galilee.

God sent the angel Gabriel to visit Mary. The angel told her, "The Lord is with you, and you are greatly favored."

Mary was troubled. She did not know what the angel meant.

Then he said, "Do not be afraid, Mary, for you have been chosen by God. You will have a Son, and you will name Him Jesus. He will be great, a king who will rule forever."

Mary was so surprised! She did not understand how this amazing thing could happen. "How can this be?" she asked.

The angel answered, "The child who will be born to you will be the Son of God. Nothing is too hard for the Lord."

And Mary believed the angel. "Let it be as you have said," she replied.

The angel of the Lord told Joseph about the coming of Jesus too. "Mary will have a Son, and you will name Him Jesus, for He will save His people from their sins," the angel said.

Joseph must have been glad to know the Savior was going to be born. He and Mary eagerly awaited the birth of Jesus.

A Wonderful Baby's Birth

Luke 2:1-39

The people of Nazareth were excited! The Roman emperor had commanded them to enroll in the town or city their families had come from. No one dared to disobey him.

Soon travelers were going in every direction. Joseph and Mary were going to Bethlehem, for they were both from the family of King David.

When they reached Bethlehem, the town was crowded with people. No place could be found for new arrivals. The long journey from Nazareth had been hard, and Mary desperately wanted a place to rest! Joseph could find only the stable of an inn. That night Baby Jesus was born. Mary wrapped Him in soft cloths, called swaddling clothes, and laid Him in a manger.

Shepherds were watching over their sheep that night near Bethlehem. Suddenly, the angel of the Lord came near, and a great light shone through the darkness. The shepherds were afraid. Why had the angel come to them?

The angel said, "Do not be afraid, for I bring you good news of great joy, which will be for all people. Today, in the city of David, a Savior has been born for you. He is Christ the Lord. And you will find the baby wrapped in swaddling clothes, lying in a manger."

This was wonderful news! Then many angels appeared and said, "Glory to God in the highest, and on earth peace, good will toward men." The angels returned to heaven, and the light faded into the still darkness of the night.

The shepherds said to each other, "Let's go to Bethlehem now and see what the Lord has told us about."

Leaving their flocks, they hurried to Bethlehem. There in a stable they found Mary, Joseph and the infant Savior. Kneeling before the manger, they worshiped the little baby who lay quietly sleeping on the hay.

On the way back to their flocks, the shepherds told everyone they met about the angel's visit and the Savior's birth.

When the baby was eight days old, Joseph and Mary named Him Jesus, the name the angel had chosen. The name Jesus means salvation.

According to Jewish law, each family had to make an offering to the Lord for their first baby boy. Rich people gave a lamb; poor people, two young pigeons. When Jesus was forty days old, Joseph and Mary took Him to the temple at Jerusalem. They offered two young pigeons to the Lord, for they were poor.

Old Simeon was in the temple. God had promised him, "You will not die until you have seen the Savior." When Mary brought Baby Jesus to the temple, God's Spirit helped Simeon know this child was the promised Savior.

Simeon came eagerly to meet Mary and took the baby in his arms. "Now may God let me depart in peace, for I have seen with my eyes the salvation which He has sent," Simeon said.

Anna was an old woman who had served God faithfully all her life. When she saw Jesus, she too gave thanks to God.

Mary never forgot what Simeon and Anna said about Jesus, nor did she forget the story the shepherds told. She thought about these things and wondered how her Son Jesus would finally become the Savior of the world.

The Wise Men Follow a Star

Matthew 2

Far to the east of Judea lived certain Wise Men who studied the stars. One night they discovered a new star, and God helped them know Jesus had been born.

These Wise Men followed God and wanted to see the child who would be the Savior of the world. At once they planned to take rich gifts and go to worship Him.

Many days they traveled across the desert to Judea. They hurried to Jerusalem, for surely the wonderful child would be in this beautiful and famous city.

Herod, the ruler, was troubled. Why did these strangers ask, "Where is the one who has been born king of the Jews? We have seen His star in the east and have come to worship Him."

Herod knew nothing about this new king. *What can this mean?* he wondered. Calling the chief priests and scribes, he demanded, "Where is the Savior to be born?"

The men remembered what the prophets had written long ago. They answered, "The Savior will be born in Bethlehem. He will rule His people."

Now Herod was even more worried. What if this new king took away his throne? Secretly, he called the Wise Men and said, "Go to Bethlehem and search for the young child. When you find Him, let me know so I may come and worship Him."

Outside the city gates, the Wise Men saw the same bright star they had seen in the east. It seemed to lead them.

At Bethlehem the star stood still over the house where Jesus lived with Mary and Joseph. At last the Wise Men had found Jesus! Falling to their knees, they worshiped Him. Opening their treasures, they gave Him rich gifts—gold, frankincense and myrrh.

Before the Wise Men left Bethlehem, God told them in a dream not to go back to Herod, so they returned to their own country by another road.

Not long afterwards, an angel of the Lord said to Joseph in a dream, "Get up, take the young child and His mother, and run to Egypt. Stay there until I tell you to return, for Herod will look for Jesus and try to kill Him." Joseph got up, took Mary and Jesus and hurried to Egypt.

Herod waited a long time for the Wise Men to return from Bethlehem, but they never came. Maybe they had guessed why he was so eager to see Jesus. Now Herod was angry! He had not found the new king!

Herod sent his soldiers to kill every child two years old or less in Bethlehem and the country round about. He thought this would get rid of Jesus, but Jesus was safe in Egypt. When Herod died, an angel told Joseph to return home, so they started back to Bethlehem.

In Judea Joseph learned that Herod's son was now ruler. What if the new king were like his father? Because Joseph was afraid, they went on to Nazareth. Here Joseph, Mary and Jesus made their home and lived in peace for many years.